'A classic is the term given to any book which comes to represent the whole universe, a book on a par with ancient talismans'

Italo Calvino

Penguin Modern Classics: The Complete List

WITH AN ESSAY BY ITALO CALVINO

PENGUIN BOOKS

PENGUIN CLASSICS

Published by the Penguin Group
Penguin Books Ltd, 80 Strand, London WC2R 0RL, England
Penguin Group (USA) Inc., 375 Hudson Street, New York, New York 10014, USA
Penguin Group (Canada), 90 Eglinton Avenue East, Suite 700, Toronto, Ontario, Canada M4P 2Y3 (a division of Pearson Penguin Canada Inc.)
Penguin Ireland, 25 St Stephen's Green, Dublin 2, Ireland (a division of Penguin Books Ltd)
Penguin Group (Australia), 250 Camberwell Road, Camberwell, Victoria 3124, Australia (a division of Pearson Australia Group Pty Ltd)
Penguin Books India Pvt Ltd, 11 Community Centre, Panchsheel Park, New Delhi – 110 017, India
Penguin Group (NZ), 67 Apollo Drive, Rosedale, Auckland 0632, New Zealand (a division of Pearson New Zealand Ltd)
Penguin Books (South Africa) (Pty) Ltd, 24 Sturdee Avenue, Rosebank, Johannesburg 2196, South Africa

Penguin Books Ltd, Registered Offices: 80 Strand, London WC2R 0RL, England

www.penguin.com

'Why Read the Classics?' first published in Italian in book form as *Perché leggere i classici* by Arnoldo Mondadori Editore S.p.A., Milan 1991
'Why Read the Classics' first published in this translation in Great Britain by Jonathan Cape 1999
Published in Penguin Classics 2009
Penguin Modern Classics: The Complete List first published in Great Britain by Penguin Classics 2011
1

Set in Monotype Dante
Typeset by Dinah Drazin
Printed in England by Clays Ltd, St Ives plc

ISBN: 978-0-141-19740-1

www.greenpenguin.co.uk

Contents

A Short History of Penguin Modern Classics

Penguin Modern Classics were born in 1961, when the renowned Penguin editor Tony Godwin decided that the great authors of the twentieth century – such as James Joyce, Joseph Conrad and Evelyn Waugh – had achieved the same classic status as Homer or Dickens, and that the reading public who enjoyed them deserved a separate list of contemporary, beautifully designed editions.

The result was Penguin Modern Classics, with their distinctive grey spines and evocative pictorial covers. Many of them were given eye-opening, avant-garde images by the legendary 60s designer Germano Facetti – a look that, after various incarnations, still inspires their current design. The first books ever pubished in this new series – including Franz Kafka's *Metamorphosis*, Carson McCuller's *The Heart is a Lonely Hunter*, F. Scott Fitzgerald's *The Great Gatsby* – are still considered landmark classics, read and loved today.

Over the years, Penguin Modern Classics have shaped the reading habits of generations. They have caused shock and outrage, inspired fantastic films, broken down social and political barriers, and sometimes pushed the boundaries of language itself. They remain an ever-evolving list of books from the last hundred (or so) years that we believe will continue to be read over and over again. From timeless authors, such as Orwell (still the bestselling writer in the series), to the addition of contemporary greats, such as John Updike, Don DeLillo, Penelope Lively, John le Carré and Ludmilla Petrushevskaya, Penguin Modern Classics continue to abide by the principle of publishing the very best, most provocative, exciting, groundbreaking, inspiring works – and constantly redefining what makes a 'classic'.

A–Z by author

* = forthcoming title after March 2011

ABBEY, EDWARD *The Monkey Wrench Gang*

ABE, KOBO *The Face of Another*

The Woman in the Dunes

ACHEBE, CHINUA *A Man of the People*

Anthills of the Savannah

Arrow of God

No Longer at Ease

The Education of a British-Protected Child

Things Fall Apart

ACKERLEY, J. R. *Hindoo Holiday*

AGEE, JAMES *A Death in the Family*

AGEE, JAMES & EVANS, WALKER *Let Us Now Praise Famous Men*

ALDISS, BRIAN *Hothouse*

ALDISS, BRIAN (Editor) *A Science Fiction Omnibus*

AMBLER, ERIC *Cause for Alarm*

Epitaph for a Spy

Journey into Fear

The Mask of Dimitrios

Uncommon Danger

AMIS, KINGSLEY *Ending Up* ⋆

Complete Stories ⋆

Girl, 20 ⋆

Lucky Jim ⋆

One Fat Englishman ⋆

The King's English ⋆

ANAND, MULK RAJ *Untouchable*

APPELFELD, AHARON *Badenheim 1939*

ARPINO, GIOVANNI *Scent of a Woman* ⋆

AYER, A. J. *Language, Truth and Logic*

BALDWIN, JAMES *Another Country*

Giovanni's Room

Go Tell It on the Mountain

Going to Meet the Man

If Beale Street Could Talk

Just Above My Head

Nobody Knows My Name

The Fire Next Time

BARBUSSE, HENRI *Under Fire*

BARTHELME, DONALD *Forty Stories*

Sixty Stories

BASSANI, GIORGIO *The Garden of the Finzi-Continis*

BATAILLE, GEORGES *Story of the Eye*

BATES, H. E. *Fair Stood the Wind for France*

De Beauvoir, Simone *Memoirs of a Dutiful Daughter*
Beckett, Samuel *First Love and Other Novellas*
Bedford, Sybille *A Legacy*
Begley, Louis *Wartime Lies*
Bellow, Saul *Collected Stories*
Dangling Man
Henderson the Rain King
Herzog
Humboldt's Gift
It All Adds Up
More Die of Heartbreak
Mr Sammler's Planet
Ravelstein
Seize the Day
The Actual
The Adventures of Augie March
The Dean's December
The Victim
To Jerusalem and Back
Benjamin, Walter *One-Way Street and Other Writings*
Benson, E. F. *Mapp and Lucia*
Bentley, Eric (Editor) *The Theory of the Modern Stage*
Berger, John *Ways of Seeing*
Bernhard, Thomas *Old Masters*
Bierce, Ambrose *The Enlarged Devil's Dictionary*

[For Blixen, Karen See Dinesen, Isak]
Blunden, Edmund *Undertones of War*
Blythe, Ronald *Akenfield*
Boetie, Dugmore *Familiarity is the Kingdom of the Lost*
Bonatti, Walter *The Mountains of My Life*
Borges, Jorge Luis *A Universal History of Iniquity*
Brodie's Report
Fictions
Labyrinths
Selected Poems
The Aleph
The Book of Sand and *Shakespeare's Memory*
The Total Library
Borowski, Tadeusz *This Way for the Gas, Ladies and Gentlemen*
Bowles, Paul *Collected Stories*
Let It Come Down
The Sheltering Sky
The Spider's House
Up Above the World
Brancati, Vitaliano *Beautiful Antonio*
Brecht, Bertolt *The Caucasian Chalk Circle*
The Good Woman of Setzuan
Brenan, Gerald *South from Granada*
Breton, André *Nadja*

Italian Folktales
Numbers in the Dark
Six Memos for the Next Millennium
The Complete Cosmicomics
The Path to the Spiders' Nests
The Road to San Giovanni
Under the Jaguar Sun
Why Read the Classics?
CALVINO, ITALO (Editor) *Fantastic Tales*
CAMUS, ALBERT *A Happy Death*
Caligula and Other Plays
Exile and the Kingdom
The Fall
The First Man
The Myth of Sisyphus
The Outsider
The Plague
The Rebel
ČAPEK, KAREL *War with the Newts*
CAPOTE, TRUMAN *A Capote Reader*
Answered Prayers
Breakfast at Tiffany's
In Cold Blood
Music for Chameleons
Other Voices, Other Rooms
Summer Crossing

The Complete Stories

Carr, J. L. *A Month in the Country*

le Carré, John *A Murder of Quality* *

A Small Town in Germany *

The Looking Glass War *

The Russia House *

The Secret Pilgrim *

The Spy Who Came in from the Cold

Carrington, Leonora *The Hearing Trumpet*

Carson, Rachel *Silent Spring*

Carter, Angela *Heroes and Villains*

The Fairy Tales of Charles Perrault

The Infernal Desire Machines of Dr Hoffman

Celan, Paul *Selected Poems*

Chandler, Raymond *The Big Sleep and Other Novels*

The Lady in the Lake and Other Novels

Chang, Eileen *Love in a Fallen City*

Lust, Caution

Chaplin, Charles *My Autobiography*

Cheever, John *Falconer*

Christopher, John *The Death of Grass*

Cioran, E. M. *A Short History of Decay*

Le Clézio, J. M. G. *Fever*

Terra Amata

The Flood

Cohen, Albert *Her Lover (Belle du Seigneur)*

COLEGATE, ISABEL *The Shooting Party*
COLLINS, NORMAN *London Belongs to Me*
COOVER, ROBERT *Briar Rose & Spanking the Maid* *
Gerald's Party *
Pricksongs and Descants *
CROSS, IAN *The God Boy*

DAHL, ROALD *Over to You*
Someone Like You
DANCHEV, ALEX (Editor) *100 Artists' Manifestos*
DAVIES, ROBERTSON *A Mixture of Frailties*
Fifth Business
Leaven of Malice
Manticore
Tempest-tost
World of Wonders
DELILLO, DON *Americana*
Libra
DENNIS, PATRICK *Auntie Mame*
DICK, PHILIP K. *The Man in the High Castle*
DINESEN, ISAK (BLIXEN, KAREN) *Anecdotes of Destiny*
Out of Africa
Seven Gothic Tales
Shadows on the Grass
The Angelic Avengers

Winter's Tales
DOCTOROW, E. L. *Ragtime*
The Book of Daniel
DOS PASSOS, JOHN *Manhattan Transfer*
Three Soldiers
U.S.A.
DRABBLE, MARGARET *A Day in the Life of a Smiling Woman* *
Jerusalem the Golden *
The Needle's Eye *
The Seven Sisters *
DREISER, THEODORE *Sister Carrie*
DREWE, ROBERT *The Bodysurfers*
DU MAURIER, DAPHNE *Don't Look Now and Other Stories*

ELLISON, RALPH *Invisible Man*
EMPSON, WILLIAM *The Complete Poems*

FALLADA, HANS *A Small Circus* *
Alone in Berlin
Iron Gustav *
Once a Jailbird *
FALUDY, GYÖRGY *My Happy Days In Hell*
FANON, FRANTZ *The Wretched of the Earth*

FARAH, NURUDDIN *From a Crooked Rib*

FITZGERALD, F. SCOTT *Flappers and Philosophers: The Collected Short Stories of F. Scott Fitzgerald*

Tender is the Night

The Beautiful and Damned

The Curious Case of Benjamin Button and Six Other Stories

The Great Gatsby

The Last Tycoon

This Side of Paradise

FITZPATRICK, PERCY *Jock of the Bushveld*

FLEMING, IAN *Casino Royale*

Diamonds are Forever

Dr No

For Your Eyes Only

From Russia with Love

Goldfinger

Live and Let Die

Moonraker

Octopussy and *The Living Daylights*

On Her Majesty's Secret Service

Quantum of Solace

The Blofeld Trilogy

The Man with the Golden Gun

The Spy Who Loved Me

Thunderball
You Only Live Twice
FORD, FORD MADOX *Parade's End*
The Fifth Queen
The Good Soldier
FRANK, ANNE *The Diary of a Young Girl*
FRAZER, JAMES *The Golden Bough*
FREUD, SIGMUND *An Outline of Psychoanalysis*
Beyond the Pleasure Principle
Civilization and Its Discontents
Interpreting Dreams
Mass Psychology
On Murder, Mourning and Melancholia
Studies in Hysteria
The Joke and Its Relation to the Unconscious
The Psychology of Love
The Psychopathology of Everyday Life
The Uncanny
The Unconscious
The 'Wolfman' and Other Cases
Wild Analysis
FREUD, SIGMUND / PHILLIPS, ADAM (Editor)
The Penguin Freud Reader
FRIEDAN, BETTY *The Feminine Mystique*
FRISCH, MAX *Homo Faber*

GALSWORTHY, JOHN *The Forsyte Saga [Vols. 1–3]*
GANDHI, M. K. *An Autobiography*
GARNER, HELEN *Monkey Grip*
GIBRAN, KAHLIL *The Prophet*
GIDE, ANDRÉ *Strait is the Gate*
The Counterfeiters
The Immoralist
GINSBERG, ALLEN *Howl, A Graphic Novel*
Howl, Kaddish and Other Poems
Selected Poems 1947–1997
GINSBERG, ALLEN & BURROUGHS, WILLIAM S.
The Yage Letters
GOSSE, EDMUND *Father and Son*
GRAVES, ROBERT *Claudius the God*
Complete Short Stories
Count Belisarius
Goodbye to All That
Homer's Daughter
I, Claudius
King Jesus
Sergeant Lamb of the Ninth
Seven Days in New Crete
The Complete Poems
The Golden Fleece
Wife to Mr Milton
GUTHRIE, WOODY *Bound for Glory*

HAMILTON, PATRICK *Hangover Square*
HAMMETT, DASHIELL *The Thin Man*
HARRISON, HARRY *Make Room! Make Room!*
HARTLEY, L. P. *The Go-between*
HEALY, JOHN *The Grass Arena*
HEISENBERG, WERNER *Physics and Philosophy*
HENRI, ADRIAN, MCGOUGH, ROGER & PATTEN, BRIAN *The Mersey Sound*
HERSEY, JOHN *Hiroshima*
HESSE, HERMANN *Siddhartha*
Steppenwolf
HIJUELOS, OSCAR *The Mambo Kings Play Songs of Love*
HIMES, CHESTER *A Rage in Harlem* *
All Shot Up *
Cotton Comes to Harlem *
The Heat's On *
The Real Cool Killers *
HINES, BARRY *A Kestrel for a Knave*
HINTON, S. E. *The Outsiders*
HOGGART, RICHARD *The Uses of Literacy*
HOLMES, JOHN CLELLON *Go*
HORNE, DONALD *The Lucky Country*
HOWARD, ROBERT E. *Heroes in the Wind: From Kull to Conan*
HOYLE, FRED *The Black Cloud*
HUGHES, DOROTHY B. *In a Lonely Place*

HUXLEY, ELSPETH *Red Strangers*

IONESCO, EUGENE *Rhinoceros, The Chairs, The Lesson*

JACKSON, SHIRLEY *The Haunting of Hill House*
The Lottery and Other Stories
We Have Always Lived in the Castle
JAFFE, RONA *The Best of Everything* *
JOLLEY, ELIZABETH *The Well*
JONES, PETER (Editor) *Imagist Poetry*
JOYCE, JAMES *A Portrait of the Artist as a Young Man*
Dubliners
Finnegans Wake
Poems and *Exiles*
Ulysses
JÜNGER, ERNST *Storm of Steel*

KAFKA, FRANZ *Amerika*
Metamorphosis and Other Stories
The Castle
The Great Wall of China
The Trial
KAPUŚCIŃSKI, RYSZARD *Another Day of Life*
Shah of Shahs
The Emperor
KARSKI, JAN *Story of a Secret State* *

KAVANAGH, PATRICK *Collected Poems*
Selected Poems
Tarry Flynn
The Green Fool
KAWABATA, YASUNARI *Beauty and Sadness*
Snow Country
The Sound of the Mountain
Thousand Cranes
KEATING, H. R. F. *Inspector Ghote Breaks an Egg* *
Inspector Ghote Trusts the Heart *
The Perfect Murder *
Under a Monsoon Cloud *
KEROUAC, JACK *Lonesome Traveler*
Maggie Cassidy
On the Road
On the Road: The Original Scroll
The Dharma Bums
The Sea is My Brother *
The Subterraneans
The Town and the City
Wake Up
KEROUAC, JACK & BURROUGHS, WILLIAM S. *And the Hippos Were Boiled in Their Tanks*
KESEY, KEN *One Flew Over the Cuckoo's Nest*
KEUN, IRMGARD *Child of All Nations*
KING, SHERWOOD *If I Die Before I Wake*

KRÚDY, GYULA *Life Is a Dream*

LAING, R. D. *The Divided Self*
LANGEWIESCHE, WILLIAM *Aloft*
LAWRENCE, T. E. *Seven Pillars of Wisdom*
LEARY, TIMOTHY, METZNER, RALPH & ALPERT, RICHARD *The Psychedelic Experience*
LEVI, CARLO *Christ Stopped at Eboli*
LEVI, PRIMO *A Tranquil Star*
If Not Now, When?
Moments of Reprieve
The Periodic Table
LITVINOFF, EMANUEL *Journey Through a Small Planet*
LIVELY, PENELOPE *According to Mark* *
Heat Wave *
Moon Tiger
Oleander, Jacaranda
LLEWELLYN, RICHARD *How Green Was My Valley*
LORCA, FEDERICO GARCÍA *Poet in New York*
Selected Poems
The House of Bernarda Alba and Other Plays
LOTT, TIM *The Scent of Dried Roses*
LOVECRAFT, H. P. *The Call of Cthulhu and Other Weird Stories*
The Dreams in the Witch House and Other Weird Stories

The Thing on the Doorstep and Other Weird Stories
LOWRY, MALCOLM *Under the Volcano*

MACDONALD, ROSS *The Underground Man* *
MACLAREN-ROSS, JULIAN *Of Love and Hunger*
MAILER, NORMAN *The Fight*
MALCOLM X *The Autobiography of Malcolm X*
MALRAUX, ANDRÉ *Man's Fate*
MAN RAY *Self-Portrait* *
MANDELA, NELSON *No Easy Walk to Freedom*
MANDELSTAM, OSIP *Selected Poems*
MANN, KLAUS *Mephisto*
MANNING, FREDERIC *The Middle Parts of Fortune*
MÁRQUEZ, GABRIEL GARCÍA *Love in the Time of Cholera*
One Hundred Years of Solitude
MARX, GROUCHO / KANFER, STEFAN (Editor) *The Essential Groucho*
MAURIAC, FRANÇOIS *Thérèse*
MCCARTHY, MARY *The Stones of Florence and Venice Observed*
MCCULLERS, CARSON *Clock Without Hands*
Reflections in a Golden Eye
The Ballad of the Sad Café
The Heart is a Lonely Hunter
The Member of the Wedding

The Mortgaged Heart

McLuhan, Marshall & Fiore, Quentin
The Medium is the Massage

McMurtry, Larry *The Last Picture Show* *

Miller, Arthur *A View from the Bridge*
After the Fall
All My Sons
Death of a Salesman
Focus
Incident at Vichy
The Crucible
The Price

Miłosz, Czesław *New and Collected Poems 1931–2001*
Proud to Be a Mammal
The Captive Mind

Mishima, Yukio *Forbidden Colours*

Mitford, Nancy *Love in a Cold Climate and Other Novels*

Mitford, Nancy & Waugh, Evelyn *The Letters of Nancy Mitford and Evelyn Waugh*

Mofolo, Thomas *Traveller to the East*

Morante, Elsa *History*

Mortimer, John *A Voyage Round My Father*
Clinging to the Wreckage
Paradise Postponed
The Sound of Trumpets

Titmuss Regained

MROŻEK, SŁAWOMIR *The Elephant*

MUNARI, BRUNO *Design as Art*

NABOKOV, VLADIMIR *Ada or Ardor*

Bend Sinister

Collected Stories

Despair

Glory

Invitation to a Beheading

King, Queen, Knave

Laughter in the Dark

Lolita

Look at the Harlequins!

Mary

Nikolai Gogol

Pale Fire

Pnin

Speak, Memory

Strong Opinions

The Annotated Lolita

The Enchanter

The Eye

The Gift

The Luzhin Defense

The Real Life of Sebastian Knight

Transparent Things

NAIPAUL, SHIVA *North of South*

NARAYAN, R. K. *The Mahabharata*

The Man-eater of Malgudi

The Painter of Signs

The Vendor of Sweets

Under the Banyan Tree and Other Stories

NERUDA, PABLO *Selected Poems*

NILAND, D'ARCY *The Shiralee*

NIN, ANAÏS *A Spy in the House of Love*

Delta of Venus

Henry and June

Little Birds

O'BRIEN, FLANN *At Swim-Two-Birds*

O'CONNOR, FRANK *An Only Child* and *My Father's Son*

My Oedipus Complex

ORWELL, GEORGE *A Clergyman's Daughter*

Animal Farm

Burmese Days

Coming Up for Air

Down and Out in Paris and London

Essays

George Orwell: A Life in Letters

Homage to Catalonia

Keep the Aspidistra Flying

Nineteen Eighty-Four
Orwell and Politics
Orwell in Spain
Orwell's England
Shooting an Elephant and Other Essays
The Complete Novels of George Orwell
The Orwell Diaries
The Road to Wigan Pier

PARK, RUTH *The Harp in the South Novels*
PARKER, DOROTHY *The Collected Dorothy Parker*
PAVEL, OTA *How I Came to Know Fish*
PAZ, OCTAVIO *The Labyrinth of Solitude*
PESSOA, FERNANDO *Selected Poems*
The Book of Disquiet
PETRUSHEVSKAYA, LUDMILLA *There Once Lived a Woman who Tried to Kill Her Neighbour's Baby*
PIRANDELLO, LUIGI *Six Characters in Search of an Author and Other Plays*
PORTER, KATHERINE ANNE *Pale Horse, Pale Rider* ★
Ship of Fools ★
POTOK, CHAIM *My Name is Asher Lev*
The Chosen
POWYS, JOHN COWPER *Wolf Solent*

PRIESTLEY, J. B. *An Inspector Calls and Other Plays*
PROUST, MARCEL *In Search of Lost Time Vol. 1: The Way by Swann's*
In Search of Lost Time Vol. 2: In the Shadow of Young Girls in Flower
In Search of Lost Time Vol. 3: The Guermantes Way
In Search of Lost Time Vol. 4: Sodom and Gomorrah
In Search of Lost Time Vol. 5: The Prisoner and *The Fugitive*
In Search of Lost Time Vol. 6: Finding Time Again

QUENEAU, RAYMOND *Zazie in the Metro*

RADIGUET, RAYMOND *Devil in the Flesh* *
RAND, AYN *Anthem*
Atlas Shrugged
The Fountainhead
We the Living
REZZORI, GREGOR VON *The Snows of Yesteryear*
RHYS, JEAN *After Leaving Mr Mackenzie*
Good Morning, Midnight
Quartet
Voyage in the Dark
Wide Sargasso Sea
RICHLER, MORDECAI *The Apprenticeship of Duddy Kravitz*

RILKE, RAINER MARIA *Letters to a Young Poet*
Selected Poems
The Notebooks of Malter Laurids Brigge
ROCHE, HENRI-PIERRE *Jules et Jim* *
ROTH, HENRY *Call it Sleep*
ROTH, JOSEPH *The Radetzky March*
RUNYON, DAMON *Guys and Dolls*
On Broadway
RYLE, GILBERT *The Concept of Mind*

SÁBATO, ERNESTO *The Tunnel* *
SAGAN, FRANÇOISE *Bonjour Tristesse* and *A Certain Smile*
SAID, EDWARD W. *Orientalism*
DE SAINT-EXUPÉRY, ANTOINE *Flight to Arras*
Southern Mail / Night Flight
Wind, Sand and Stars
SAKI, *The Complete Short Stories*
SALIH, TAYEB *Season of Migration to the North*
SALTER, JAMES *Light Years*
Solo Faces
The Hunters
SARTRE, JEAN-PAUL *Huis Clos and Other Plays*
Iron in the Soul
Modern Times
Nausea

The Age of Reason
The Reprieve
Words
SCHNEIDER, PETER *The Wall Jumper*
SCHNITZLER, ARTHUR *Dream Story*
SCULLY, WILLIAM *Unconventional Reminiscences*
SEARLE, RONALD *St Trinian's*
The Terror of St Trinian's and Other Drawings
SELBY JR, HUBERT *Last Exit to Brooklyn* *
The Demon *
The Room *
SELVON, SAM *Moses Ascending*
The Lonely Londoners
SHAFFER, PETER *Amadeus*
Equus
The Royal Hunt of the Sun
SHALAMOV, VARLAM *Kolyma Tales*
SHERRIFF, R. C. *Journey's End*
SIMENON, GEORGES *Maigret and the Ghost*
SINCLAIR, UPTON *Oil!*
SINGER, ISAAC BASHEVIS *Collected Stories* *
SKELTON, ROBIN (Editor) *Poetry of the Thirties*
SKVORECKY, JOSEF *The Cowards*
SMITH, STEVIE *Selected Poems*
SOLZHENITSYN, ALEKSANDR *One Day in the Life of Ivan Denisovich*

SONTAG, SUSAN *Against Interpretation and Other Essays*
Death Kit
Illness as Metaphor and *AIDS and Its Metaphors*
In America
On Photography
Styles of Radical Will
The Benefactor
The Volcano Lover
Under the Sign of Saturn
Where the Stress Falls
SPARK, MURIEL *The Ballad of Peckham Rye*
The Driver's Seat
The Prime of Miss Jean Brodie
STEGNER, WALLACE *Angle of Repose*
Crossing to Safety
STEIN, GERTRUDE *The Autobiography of Alice B. Toklas*
Three Lives
STEINBECK, JOHN *A Life in Letters*
A Russian Journal
Burning Bright
Cannery Row
East of Eden
In Dubious Battle
Journal of a Novel
Of Mice and Men
Once There Was a War

Sweet Thursday
The Acts of King Arthur and his Noble Knights
The Grapes of Wrath
The Log from the Sea of Cortez
The Long Valley
The Moon is Down
The Pastures of Heaven
The Pearl
The Red Pony
The Short Reign of Pippin IV
The Wayward Bus
The Winter of Our Discontent
To a God Unknown
Tortilla Flat
Travels with Charley

STOW, RANDOLPH *The Merry-Go-Round in the Sea*
SÜSKIND, PATRICK *Perfume*
SVEVO, ITALO *Zeno's Conscience*
SYNGE, J. M. *The Aran Islands*

TAGORE, RABINDRANATH *He*
TALESE, GAY *Frank Sinatra Has a Cold and Other Essays*
TEVIS, WALTER *The Hustler*
The Man Who Fell to Earth
The Queen's Gambit

THEROUX, PAUL *The Great Railway Bazaar*
The Old Patagonian Express
THIONG'O, NGŨGĨ WA *A Grain of Wheat*
Petals of Blood
THOMAS, DYLAN *Selected Poems*
Under Milk Wood
THOMAS, R. S. *Selected Poems*
THOMPSON, FLORA *Lark Rise to Candleford*
THOMPSON, HUNTER S. *Hell's Angels*
TOOLE, JOHN KENNEDY *A Confederacy of Dunces*
TRESSELL, ROBERT *The Ragged Trousered Philanthropists*
TRUMBO, DALTON *Johnny Got His Gun*

UPDIKE, JOHN *A Month of Sundays*
Brazil
Couples
In the Beauty of the Lilies
Marry Me
Memories of the Ford Administration
Rabbit at Rest
Rabbit is Rich
Rabbit Redux
Rabbit, Run
Roger's Version
S.

The Centaur
The Complete Henry Bech
The Coup
The Poorhouse Fair
The Witches of Eastwick
Toward the End of Time

VIZINCZEY, STEPHEN *In Praise of Older Women*
VONNEGUT, KURT *Cat's Cradle*

WALSER, ROBERT *The Assistant*
WARHOL, ANDY *America*
POPism
The Andy Warhol Diaries
The Philosophy of Andy Warhol
WARREN, ROBERT PENN *All the King's Men*
WAUGH, EVELYN *A Handful of Dust*
A Little Learning: The First Volume of an Autobiography
A Little Order
Black Mischief
Brideshead Revisited
Decline and Fall
Helena
Labels
Men at Arms
Officers and Gentlemen

Put Out More Flags
Remote People
Scoop
Sword of Honour
The Complete Short Stories of Evelyn Waugh
The Loved One
The Ordeal of Gilbert Pinfold
Unconditional Surrender
Vile Bodies
Waugh in Abyssinia
When the Going was Good
Work Suspended and Other Stories

WAUGH, EVELYN & MITFORD, NANCY *The Letters of Nancy Mitford and Evelyn Waugh*

WEBB, CHARLES *The Graduate*

WEIL, SIMONE *Simone Weil: An Anthology*

WELTY, EUDORA *The Golden Apples* *

WEST, NATHANAEL *The Day of the Locust* and *The Dream Life of Balso Snell*

WIESEL, ELIE *Night*

WILDER, THORNTON *Our Town and Other Plays*
The Bridge of San Luis Rey

WILLANS, GEOFFREY & SEARLE, RONALD *Molesworth*

WILLIAMS, TENNESSEE *A Streetcar Named Desire*
Baby Doll and Other Plays
Cat on a Hot Tin Roof

Memoirs
Mister Paradise
Suddenly Last Summer and Other Plays
Sweet Bird of Youth and Other Plays
The Glass Menagerie
The Rose Tattoo and Other Plays
WILLIAMS, WILLIAM CARLOS *Selected Poems*
WILLIAMSON, HENRY *Tarka the Otter*
WILSON, SLOAN *The Man in the Gray Flannel Suit*
WODEHOUSE, P. G. *Heavy Weather*
WOOLF, VIRGINIA *A Room of One's Own*
A Room of One's Own / Three Guineas
Between the Acts
Mrs Dalloway
Orlando
Selected Short Stories
The Waves
The Years
To the Lighthouse
WYNDHAM, JOHN *Chocky*
The Chrysalids
The Day of the Triffids

YEATS, W. B. *Selected Plays*
Selected Poems
Writings on Irish Folklore, Legend and Myth

YOUNG, MICHAEL & WILLMOTT, PETER *Family and Kinship in East London*
YOURCENAR, MARGUERITE *Memoirs of Hadrian*

ZHONGSHU, QIAN *Fortress Besieged*

Why Read the Classics?

ITALO CALVINO

Let us begin by putting forward some definitions.

1. *The classics are those books about which you usually hear people saying: 'I'm rereading . . .', never 'I'm reading . . .'*

At least this is the case with those people whom one presumes are 'well read'; it does not apply to the young, since they are at an age when their contact with the world, and with the classics which are part of that world, is important precisely because it is their first such contact.

The iterative prefix 're-' in front of the verb 'read' can represent a small act of hypocrisy on the part of people ashamed to admit they have not read a famous book. To reassure them, all one need do is to point out that however wide-ranging any person's formative reading may be, there will always be an enormous number of fundamental works that one has not read.

Put up your hand anyone who has read the whole of Herodotus and Thucydides. And what about Saint-Simon? and Cardinal Retz? Even the great cycles of nineteenth-century novels are more often mentioned than read. In France they start to read Balzac at school, and judging by the number of editions in circulation people apparently continue to read him long after the end of their schooldays. But if there were an official survey on Balzac's popularity in Italy, I am afraid he would figure very low down the list. Fans of Dickens in Italy are a small elite who whenever they meet start to reminisce about characters and episodes as though talking of people they actually knew. When Michel Butor was teaching in the United States a number of years ago, he became so tired of people asking him about Émile Zola, whom he had never read, that he made up his mind to read the whole cycle of Rougon-Macquart novels. He discovered that it was entirely different from how he had imagined it: it turned out to be a fabulous, mythological genealogy and cosmogony, which he then described in a brilliant article.

What this shows is that reading a great work for the first time when one is fully adult is an extraordinary pleasure, one which is very different (though it is impossible to say whether more or less pleasurable) from reading it in one's youth. Youth endows every reading, as it does every experience, with a unique flavour and significance, whereas at a mature age one appreciates (or should appreciate) many more details, levels and meanings. We can therefore try out this other formulation of our definition:

2. *The classics are those books which constitute a treasured experience for those who have read and loved them; but they remain just as rich an experience for those who reserve the chance to read them for when they are in the best condition to enjoy them.*

For the fact is that the reading we do when young can often be of little value because we are impatient, cannot concentrate, lack expertise in how to read, or because we lack experience of life. This youthful reading can be (perhaps at the same time) literally formative in that it gives a form or shape to our future experiences, providing them with models, ways of dealing with them, terms of comparison, schemes for categorising them, scales of value, paradigms of beauty: all things which continue to operate in us even when we remember little or nothing about the book we read when young. When we reread the book in our maturity, we then rediscover these constants which by now form part of our inner mechanisms though we have forgotten where they came from. There is a particular potency in the work which can be forgotten in itself but which leaves its seed behind in us. The definition which we can now give is this:

3. The classics are books which exercise a particular influence, both when they imprint themselves on our imagination as unforgettable, and when they hide in the layers of memory disguised as the individual's or the collective unconscious.

For this reason there ought to be a time in one's adult life which is dedicated to rediscovering the most important readings of our youth. Even if the books remain the same (though they too change, in the light of an altered historical perspective), we certainly have changed, and this later encounter is therefore completely new.

Consequently, whether one uses the verb 'to read' or the verb 'to reread' is not really so important. We could in fact say:

4. A classic is a book which with each rereading offers as much of a sense of discovery as the first reading.

5. A classic is a book which even when we read it for the first time gives the sense of rereading something we have read before.

Definition 4 above can be considered a corollary of this one:

6. A classic is a book which has never exhausted all it has to say to its readers.

Whereas definition 5 suggests a more elaborate formulation, such as this:

7. The classics are those books which come to us bearing the aura of previous interpretations, and trailing behind them the traces they have left in the culture or cultures (or just in the languages and customs) through which they have passed.

This applies both to ancient and modern classics. If I read *The Odyssey*, I read Homer's text but I cannot forget all the things that Ulysses' adventures have come to mean in the course of the centuries, and I cannot help wondering whether these meanings were implicit in the original text or if they are later accretions, deformations or expansions of it. If I read Kafka, I find myself approving or rejecting the legitimacy of the adjective 'Kafkaesque' which we hear constantly being used to refer to just about anything. If I read Turgenev's *Fathers and Sons* or Dostoevsky's *The Devils* I cannot help reflecting on how the characters in these books have continued to be reincarnated right down to our own times.

Reading a classic must also surprise us, when we compare it to the image we previously had of it. That is why we can never recommend enough a first-hand reading of the text itself, avoiding as far as possible secondary bibliography, commentaries and other interpretations. Schools and universities should hammer home the idea that no book which discusses another book can ever say more than the original book under discussion; yet they actually do everything to make students believe the opposite. There is a reversal of values here which is very widespread, which means that the introduction, critical apparatus and bibliography are used like a smoke-screen to conceal what the text has to say and what it can only say if it is left to speak without intermediaries who claim to know more than the text itself. We can conclude, therefore, that:

8. A classic is a work which constantly generates a pulviscular cloud of critical discourse around it, but which always shakes the particles off.

A classic does not necessarily teach us something that we did not know already; sometimes we discover in a classic something which we had always known (or had always thought we knew) but did not realise that the classic text had said it first (or that the idea was connected with that text in a particular way). And this discovery is also a very gratifying surprise, as is always the case when we learn the source of an idea, or its connection with a text, or who said it first. From all this we could derive a definition like this:

9. *Classics are books which, the more we think we know them through hearsay, the more original, unexpected and innovative we find them when we actually read them.*

Of course, this happens when a classic text 'works' as a classic, that is when it establishes a personal relationship with the reader. If there is no spark, the exercise is pointless: it is no use reading classics out of a sense of duty or respect, we should only read them for love. Except at school: school has to teach you to know, whether you like it or not, a certain number of classics amongst which (or by using them as a benchmark) you will later recognise 'your' own classics. School is obliged to provide you with the tools to enable you to make your own choice; but the only choices which count are those which you take after or outside any schooling.

It is only during unenforced reading that you will come across the book which will become 'your' book. I know an excellent art historian, an enormously well-read man, who out of all the volumes he has read is fondest of all of *The Pickwick Papers*, quoting lines from Dickens' book during any discussion, and relating every event in his life to episodes in Pickwick. Gradually he himself, the universe and its real philosophy have all taken the form of *The Pickwick Papers* in a process of total identification. If we go down this road we arrive at an idea of a classic which is very lofty and demanding:

10. A classic is the term given to any book which comes to represent the whole universe, a book on a par with ancient talismans.

A definition such as this brings us close to the idea of the total book, of the kind dreamt of by Mallarmé. But a classic can also establish an equally powerful relationship not of identity but of opposition or antithesis. All of Jean-Jacques Rousseau's thoughts and actions are dear to me, but they all arouse in me an irrepressible urge to contradict, criticise and argue with him. Of course, this is connected with the fact that I find his personality so uncongenial to my temperament, but if that were all, I would simply avoid reading him; whereas in fact I cannot help regarding him as one of my authors. What I will say, then, is this:

11. 'Your' classic is a book to which you cannot remain indifferent, and which helps you define yourself in relation or even in opposition to it.

I do not believe I need justify my use of the term 'classic' which makes no distinction in terms of antiquity, style or authority. (For the history of all these meanings of the term, there is an exhaustive entry on 'Classico' by Franco Fortini in the *Enciclopedia Einaudi*, vol. III.) For the sake of my argument here, what distinguishes a classic is perhaps only a kind of resonance we perceive emanating either from an ancient or a modern work, but one which has its own place in a cultural continuum. We could say:

12. *A classic is a work that comes before other classics; but those who have read other classics first immediately recognise its place in the genealogy of classic works.*

At this point I can no longer postpone the crucial problem of how to relate the reading of classics to the reading of all the other texts which are not classics. This is a problem which is linked to questions like: 'Why read the classics instead of reading works which will give us a deeper understanding of our own times?' and 'Where can we find the time and the ease of mind to read the classics, inundated as we are by the flood of printed material about the present?'

Of course, hypothetically the lucky reader may exist who can dedicate the 'reading time' of his or her days solely to Lucretius, Lucian, Montaigne, Erasmus, Quevedo, Marlowe, the *Discourse on Method*, Goethe's *Wilhelm Meister*, Coleridge, Ruskin, Proust and Valéry, with the occasional sortie into Murasaki or the Icelandic Sagas. And presumably that person can do all this without having to write reviews of the latest reprint, submit articles in the pursuit of a university chair, or send in work for a publisher with an imminent deadline.

For this regime to continue without any contamination, the lucky person would have to avoid reading the newspapers, and never be tempted by the latest novel or the most recent sociological survey. But it remains to be seen to what extent such rigour could be justified or even found useful. The contemporary world may be banal and stultifying, but it is always the context in which we have to place ourselves to look either backwards or forwards. In order to read the classics, you have to establish where exactly you are reading them 'from', otherwise both the reader and the text tend to drift in a timeless haze. So what we can say is that the person who derives maximum benefit from a reading of the classics is the one who skilfully alternates classic readings with calibrated doses of contemporary material. And this does not necessarily presuppose someone with a harmonious inner calm: it could also be the result of an impatient, nervy temperament, of someone constantly irritated and dissatisfied.

Perhaps the ideal would be to hear the present as a noise outside our window, warning us of the traffic jams and weather changes outside, while we continue to follow the discourse of the classics which resounds clearly and articulately inside our room. But it is already an achievement for most people to hear the classics as a distant echo, outside the room which is pervaded by the present as if it were a television set on at full volume. We should therefore add:

13. A classic is a work which relegates the noise of the present to a background hum, which at the same time the classics cannot exist without.

14. A classic is a work which persists as background noise even when a present that is totally incompatible with it holds sway.

The fact remains that reading the classics seems to be at odds with our pace of life, which does not tolerate long stretches of time, or the space for humanist *otium*; and also with the eclecticism of our culture which would never be able to draw up a catalogue of classic works to suit our own times.

Instead these were exactly the conditions of Leopardi's life: living in his father's castle (his 'paterno ostello'), he was able to pursue his cult of Greek and Latin antiquity with his father Monaldo's formidable library, to which he added the entirety of Italian literature up to that time, and all of French literature except for novels and the most recently published works, which were relegated to its margins, for the comfort of his sister ('your Stendhal' is how he talked of the French novelist to Paolina). Giacomo satisfied even his keenest scientific and historical enthusiasms with texts that were never exactly 'up to date', reading about the habits of birds in Buffon, about Frederik Ruysch's mummies in Fontenelle, and Columbus' travels in Robertson.

Today a classical education like that enjoyed by the young Leopardi is unthinkable, particularly as the library of his father Count Monaldo has disintegrated. Disintegrated both in the sense that the old titles have been decimated, and in that the new ones have proliferated in all modern literatures and cultures. All that can be done is for each one of us to invent our own ideal library of our classics; and I would say that one half of it should consist of books we have read and that have meant something for us, and the other half of books which we intend to read and which we suppose might mean something to us. We should also leave a section of empty spaces for surprises and chance discoveries.

I notice that Leopardi is the only name from Italian literature that I have cited. This is the effect of the disintegration of the library. Now I ought to rewrite the whole article making it quite clear that the classics help us understand who we are and the point we have reached, and that consequently Italian classics are indispensable to us Italians in order to compare them with foreign classics, and foreign classics are equally indispensable so that we can measure them against Italian classics.

After that I should really rewrite it a third time, so that people do not believe that the classics must be read because they serve some purpose. The only reason that can be adduced in their favour is that reading the classics is always better than not reading them.

And if anyone objects that they are not worth all that effort, I will cite Cioran (not a classic, at least not yet, but a contemporary thinker who is only now being translated into Italian): 'While the hemlock was being prepared, Socrates was learning a melody on the flute. "What use will that be to you?" he was asked. "At least I will learn this melody before I die." '

Italo Calvino, 1981

A–Z by title

100 ARTISTS' MANIFESTOS Alex Danchev (Editor)
ACCORDING TO MARK * Penelope Lively
THE ACTS OF KING ARTHUR AND HIS NOBLE KNIGHTS John Steinbeck
THE ACTUAL Saul Bellow
ADA OR ARDOR Vladimir Nabokov
THE ADVENTURES OF AUGIE MARCH Saul Bellow
AFTER LEAVING MR MACKENZIE Jean Rhys
AFTER THE FALL Arthur Miller
AGAINST INTERPRETATION AND OTHER ESSAYS Susan Sontag
THE AGE OF REASON Jean-Paul Sartre
AKENFIELD Ronald Blythe
THE ALEPH Jorge Luis Borges
ALL MY SONS Arthur Miller
ALL SHOT UP * Chester Himes
ALL THE KING'S MEN Robert Penn Warren
ALOFT William Langewiesche
ALONE IN BERLIN Hans Fallada
AMADEUS Peter Shaffer

AMERICA Andy Warhol
AMERICANA Don DeLillo
AMERIKA Franz Kafka
THE ANNOTATED LOLITA Vladimir Nabokov
AN AUTOBIOGRAPHY M. K. Gandhi
AN INSPECTOR CALLS AND OTHER PLAYS J. B. Priestley
AN ONLY CHILD *and* MY FATHER'S SON Frank O'Connor
AN OUTLINE OF PSYCHOANALYSIS Sigmund Freud
AND THE HIPPOS WERE BOILED IN THEIR TANKS William Burroughs & Jack Kerouac
THE ANDY WARHOL DIARIES Andy Warhol
ANECDOTES OF DESTINY Isak Dinesen (Karen Blixen)
THE ANGELIC AVENGERS Isak Dinesen (Karen Blixen)
ANGLE OF REPOSE Wallace Stegner
ANIMAL FARM George Orwell
ANOTHER COUNTRY James Baldwin
ANOTHER DAY OF LIFE Ryszard Kapuściński
ANSWERED PRAYERS Truman Capote
ANTHEM Ayn Rand
ANTHILLS OF THE SAVANNAH Chinua Achebe
THE APPRENTICESHIP OF DUDDY KRAVITZ Mordecai Richler
THE ARAN ISLANDS J. M. Synge
ARROW OF GOD Chinua Achebe

THE ASSISTANT Robert Walser
AT SWIM-TWO-BIRDS Flann O'Brien
ATLAS SHRUGGED Ayn Rand
AUNTIE MAME Patrick Dennis
THE AUTOBIOGRAPHY OF ALICE B. TOKLAS Gertrude Stein
THE AUTOBIOGRAPHY OF MALCOLM X Malcolm X

BABY DOLL AND OTHER PLAYS Tennessee Williams
BADENHEIM 1939 Aharon Appelfeld
THE BALLAD OF PECKHAM RYE Muriel Spark
THE BALLAD OF THE SAD CAFÉ Carson McCullers
THE BEAUTIFUL AND DAMNED F. Scott Fitzgerald
BEAUTIFUL ANTONIO Vitaliano Brancati
BEAUTY AND SADNESS Yasunari Kawabata
BEND SINISTER Vladimir Nabokov
THE BENEFACTOR Susan Sontag
THE BEST OF EVERYTHING * Rona Jaffe
BETWEEN THE ACTS Virginia Woolf
BEYOND THE PLEASURE PRINCIPLE Sigmund Freud
THE BIG SLEEP AND OTHER NOVELS Raymond Chandler
THE BLACK CLOUD Fred Hoyle
BLACK MISCHIEF Evelyn Waugh
THE BLOFELD TRILOGY Ian Fleming
THE BODYSURFERS Robert Drewe

BONJOUR TRISTESSE *and* A CERTAIN SMILE Françoise Sagan
THE BOOK OF DANIEL E. L. Doctorow
THE BOOK OF DISQUIET Fernando Pessoa
THE BOOK OF SAND *and* SHAKESPEARE'S MEMORY Jorge Luis Borges
BOUND FOR GLORY Woody Guthrie
BRAZIL John Updike
BREAKFAST AT TIFFANY'S Truman Capote
BRIAR ROSE & SPANKING THE MAID * Robert Coover
BRIDESHEAD REVISITED Evelyn Waugh
THE BRIDGE OF SAN LUIS REY Thornton Wilder
BRODIE'S REPORT Jorge Luis Borges
BURMESE DAYS George Orwell
BURNING BRIGHT John Steinbeck

CALIGULA AND OTHER PLAYS Albert Camus
CALL IT SLEEP Henry Roth
THE CALL OF CTHULHU AND OTHER WEIRD STORIES H. P. Lovecraft
CANNERY ROW John Steinbeck
A CAPOTE READER Truman Capote
THE CAPTIVE MIND Czesław Miłosz
CASINO ROYALE Ian Fleming
THE CASTLE Franz Kafka
THE CAT INSIDE William S. Burroughs

Cat on a Hot Tin Roof Tennessee Williams
Cat's Cradle Kurt Vonnegut
Cattle Thief Frank Brownlee
The Caucasian Chalk Circle Bertolt Brecht
Cause for Alarm Eric Ambler
The Centaur John Updike
Child of All Nations Irmgard Keun
Chocky John Wyndham
The Chosen Chaim Potok
Christ Stopped at Eboli Carol Levi
The Chrysalids John Wyndham
Cities of the Red Night William S. Burroughs
Civilization and Its Discontents Sigmund Freud
Claudius the God Robert Graves
A Clergyman's Daughter George Orwell
Clinging to the Wreckage John Mortimer
Clock Without Hands Carson McCullers
A Clockwork Orange Anthony Burgess
The Collected Dorothy Parker Dorothy Parker
Collected Poems 1947–1997 Allen Ginsberg
Collected Poems Patrick Kavanagh
Collected Stories Saul Bellow
Collected Stories Paul Bowles
Collected Stories Vladimir Nabokov
Collected Stories * Isaac Bashevis Singer
Complete Stories * Kingsley Amis

COMING UP FOR AIR George Orwell
THE COMPLETE COSMICOMICS Italo Calvino
THE COMPLETE HENRY BECH John Updike
THE COMPLETE NOVELS OF GEORGE ORWELL George Orwell
THE COMPLETE POEMS William Empson
THE COMPLETE POEMS Robert Graves
COMPLETE SHORT STORIES Robert Graves
THE COMPLETE SHORT STORIES Saki
THE COMPLETE SHORT STORIES OF EVELYN WAUGH Evelyn Waugh
THE COMPLETE STORIES Truman Capote
THE CONCEPT OF MIND Gilbert Ryle
A CONFEDERACY OF DUNCES John Kennedy Toole
COTTON COMES TO HARLEM * Chester Himes
COUNT BELISARIUS Robert Graves
THE COUNTERFEITERS André Gide
THE COUP John Updike
COUPLES John Updike
THE COWARDS Josef Skvorecky
CROSSING TO SAFETY Wallace Stegner
THE CRUCIBLE Arthur Miller
THE CURIOUS CASE OF BENJAMIN BUTTON AND SIX OTHER STORIES F. Scott Fitzgerald

DANGLING MAN Saul Bellow

A Day in the Life of a Smiling Woman * Margaret Drabble
The Day of the Locust *and* The Dream Life of Balso Snell Nathanael West
The Day of the Triffids John Wyndham
The Dean's December Saul Bellow
A Death in the Family James Agee
Death Kit Susan Sontag
Death of a Salesman Arthur Miller
The Death of Grass John Christopher
Decline and Fall Evelyn Waugh
Delta of Venus Anaïs Nin
The Demon * Hubert Selby Jr
Design as Art Bruno Munari
Despair Vladimir Nabokov
Devil in the Flesh * Raymond Radiguet
The Dharma Bums Jack Kerouac
Diamonds are Forever Ian Fleming
The Diary of a Young Girl Anne Frank
The Divided Self R. Laing
Don't Look Now and Other Stories Daphne du Maurier
Down and Out in Paris and London George Orwell
Dr No Ian Fleming
Dream Story Arthur Schnitzler

THE DREAMS IN THE WITCH HOUSE AND OTHER WEIRD STORIES H. P. Lovecraft
THE DRIVER'S SEAT Muriel Spark
THE DIVIDED SELF R. D. Laing
DUBLINERS James Joyce

EAST OF EDEN John Steinbeck
THE EDUCATION OF A BRITISH-PROTECTED CHILD Chinua Achebe
THE ELEPHANT Sławomir Mrożek
THE EMPEROR Ryszard Kapuściński
THE EMPTY SPACE Peter Brook
THE ENCHANTER Vladimir Nabokov
ENDING UP * Kingsley Amis
THE ENLARGED DEVIL'S DICTIONARY Ambrose Bierce
EPITAPH FOR A SPY Eric Ambler
EQUUS Peter Shaffer
ESSAYS George Orwell
THE ESSENTIAL GROUCHO Groucho Marx/Stefan Kanfer (Editor)
EXILE AND THE KINGDOM Albert Camus
EXTERMINATOR! William S. Burroughs
THE EYE Vladimir Nabokov

THE FACE OF ANOTHER Kobo Abe
FAIR STOOD THE WIND FOR FRANCE H. E. Bates

The Fairy Tales of Charles Perrault Angela Carter
Falconer John Cheever
The Fall Albert Camus
Familiarity is the Kingdom of the Lost Dugmore Boetie
Family and Kinship in East London Michael Young & Peter Willmott
Fantastic Tales Italo Calvino (Editor)
Father and Son Edmund Gosse
The Feminine Mystique Betty Friedan
Fever J. M. G. Le Clézio
Fictions Jorge Luis Borges
Fifth Business Robertson Davies
The Fifth Queen Ford Madox Ford
The Fight Norman Mailer
Finnegans Wake James Joyce
The Fire Next Time James Baldwin
First Love and Other Novellas Samuel Beckett
The First Man Albert Camus
Flappers and Philosophers: The Collected Short Stories of F. Scott Fitzgerald F. Scott Fitzgerald
Flight to Arras Antoine de Saint-Exupéry
The Flood J. M. G. Le Clézio
Focus Arthur Miller

FOR YOUR EYES ONLY Ian Fleming
FORBIDDEN COLOURS Yukio Mishima
THE FORSYTE SAGA [VOLS. 1–3] John Galsworthy
FORTRESS BESIEGED Qian Zhongshu
FORTY STORIES Donald Barthelme
THE FOUNTAINHEAD Ayn Rand
FRANK SINATRA HAS A COLD AND OTHER ESSAYS Gay Talese
FROM A CROOKED RIB Nuruddin Farah
FROM RUSSIA WITH LOVE Ian Fleming

THE GARDEN OF THE FINZI-CONTINIS Giorgio Bassani
GEORGE ORWELL: A LIFE IN LETTERS George Orwell
GERALD'S PARTY * Robert Coover
THE GIFT Vladimir Nabokov
GIOVANNI'S ROOM James Baldwin
GIRL, 20 * Kingsley Amis
THE GLASS MENAGERIE Tennessee Williams
GLORY Vladimir Nabokov
GO John Clellon Holmes
GO TELL IT ON THE MOUNTAIN James Baldwin
THE GO-BETWEEN L. P. Hartley
THE GOD BOY Ian Cross
GOING TO MEET THE MAN James Baldwin
THE GOLDEN APPLES * Eudora Welty

THE GOLDEN BOUGH James Frazer
THE GOLDEN FLEECE Robert Graves
GOLDFINGER Ian Fleming
GOOD MORNING, MIDNIGHT Jean Rhys
THE GOOD SOLDIER Ford Madox Ford
THE GOOD WOMAN OF SETZUAN Bertolt Brecht
GOODBYE TO ALL THAT Robert Graves
THE GRADUATE Charles Webb
A GRAIN OF WHEAT Ngũgĩ wa Thiong'o
THE GRAPES OF WRATH John Steinbeck
THE GRASS ARENA John Healy
THE GREAT GATSBY F. Scott Fitzgerald
THE GREAT RAILWAY BAZAAR Paul Theroux
THE GREAT WALL OF CHINA Franz Kafka
THE GREEN FOOL Patrick Kavanagh
GUYS AND DOLLS Damon Runyon

A HANDFUL OF DUST Evelyn Waugh
HANGOVER SQUARE Patrick Hamilton
A HAPPY DEATH Albert Camus
THE HARP IN THE SOUTH NOVELS Ruth Park
THE HAUNTING OF HILL HOUSE Shirley Jackson
HE Rabindranath Tagore
THE HEARING TRUMPET Leonora Carrington
THE HEART IS A LONELY HUNTER Carson McCullers
HEAT WAVE * Penelope Lively

THE HEAT'S ON * Chester Himes
HEAVY WEATHER P. G. Wodehouse
HELENA Evelyn Waugh
HELL'S ANGELS Hunter S. Thompson
HENDERSON THE RAIN KING Saul Bellow
HENRY AND JUNE Anaïs Nin
HER LOVER (BELLE DU SEIGNEUR) Albert Cohen
HERMIT IN PARIS Italo Calvino
HEROES AND VILLAINS Angela Carter
HEROES IN THE WIND: FROM KULL TO CONAN
Robert E. Howard
HERZOG Saul Bellow
HINDOO HOLIDAY J. R. Ackerley
HIROSHIMA John Hersey
HISTORY Elsa Morante
HOMAGE TO CATALONIA George Orwell
HOMER'S DAUGHTER Robert Graves
HOMO FABER Max Frisch
HOTHOUSE Brain Aldiss
THE HOUSE OF BERNARDA ALBA AND OTHER PLAYS
Federico García Lorca
HOW GREEN WAS MY VALLEY Richard Llewellyn
HOW I CAME TO KNOW FISH Ota Pavel
HOWL, A GRAPHIC NOVEL Allen Ginsberg
HOWL, KADDISH AND OTHER POEMS Allen Ginsberg
HUIS CLOS AND OTHER PLAYS Jean-Paul Sartre

HUMBOLDT'S GIFT Saul Bellow
THE HUNTERS James Salter
THE HUSTLER Walter Tevis
I, CLAUDIUS Robert Graves
IF BEALE STREET COULD TALK James Baldwin
IF I DIE BEFORE I WAKE Sherwood King
IF NOT NOW, WHEN? Primo Levi
ILLNESS AS METAPHOR *and* AIDS AND ITS METAPHORS Susan Sontag
IMAGIST POETRY Peter Jones (Editor)
THE IMMORALIST
IN A LONELY PLACE Dorothy B. Hughes
IN AMERICA Susan Sontag
IN COLD BLOOD Truman Capote
IN DUBIOUS BATTLE John Steinbeck
IN PRAISE OF OLDER WOMEN Stephen Vizinczey
IN SEARCH OF LOST TIME VOL. 1: THE WAY BY SWANN'S Marcel Proust
IN SEARCH OF LOST TIME VOL. 2: IN THE SHADOW OF YOUNG GIRLS IN FLOWER Marcel Proust
IN SEARCH OF LOST TIME VOL. 3: THE GUERMANTES WAY Marcel Proust
IN SEARCH OF LOST TIME VOL. 4: SODOM AND GOMORRAH Marcel Proust
IN SEARCH OF LOST TIME VOL. 5: THE PRISONER *and* THE FUGITIVE Marcel Proust

IN SEARCH OF LOST TIME VOL. 6: FINDING TIME AGAIN Marcel Proust
IN THE BEAUTY OF THE LILIES John Updike
INCIDENT AT VICHY Arthur Miller
THE INFERNAL DESIRE MACHINES OF DR HOFFMAN Angela Carter
INSPECTOR GHOTE BREAKS AN EGG * H. R. F. Keating
INSPECTOR GHOTE TRUSTS THE HEART * H. R. F. Keating
INTERPRETING DREAMS Sigmund Freud
INTERZONE William S. Burroughs
INTO THE WAR * Italo Calvino
INVISIBLE MAN Ralph Ellison
INVITATION TO A BEHEADING Vladimir Nabokov
IRON GUSTAV * Hans Fallada
IRON IN THE SOUL Jean-Paul Sartre
IT ALL ADDS UP Saul Bellow
ITALIAN FOLKTALES Italo Calvino

JERUSALEM THE GOLDEN * Margaret Drabble
THE JOB William S. Burroughs
JOCK OF THE BUSHVELD Percy Fitzpatrick
JOHNNY GOT HIS GUN Dalton Trumbo
THE JOKE AND ITS RELATION TO THE UNCONSCIOUS Sigmund Freud

JOURNAL OF A NOVEL John Steinbeck
JOURNEY INTO FEAR Eric Ambler
JOURNEY THROUGH A SMALL PLANET Emanuel Litvinoff
JOURNEY'S END R. C. Sherriff
JULES ET JIM * Henri-Pierre Roche
JUNKY William S. Burroughs
JUST ABOVE MY HEAD James Baldwin

KEEP THE ASPIDISTRA FLYING George Orwell
A KESTREL FOR A KNAVE Barry Hines
KING JESUS Robert Graves
KING, QUEEN, KNAVE Vladimir Nabokov
THE KING'S ENGLISH * Kingsley Amis
KOLYMA TALES Varlam Shalamov

LABELS Evelyn Waugh
THE LABYRINTH OF SOLITUDE Octavio Paz
LABYRINTHS Jorge Luis Borges
THE LADY IN THE LAKE AND OTHER NOVELS Raymond Chandler
LANGUAGE, TRUTH AND LOGIC A. J. Ayer
LARK RISE TO CANDLEFORD Flora Thompson
LAST EXIT TO BROOKLYN * Hubert Selby Jr
THE LAST PICTURE SHOW * Larry McMurtry

THE LAST TYCOON F. Scott Fitzgerald
LAUGHTER IN THE DARK Vladimir Nabokov
LEAVEN OF MALICE Robertson Davies
A LEGACY Sybille Bedford
LESS THAN ONE * Joseph Brodsky
LET IT COME DOWN Paul Bowles
LET US NOW PRAISE FAMOUS MEN James Agee & Walker Evans
LETTERS 1945–59 William S. Burroughs
THE LETTERS OF NANCY MITFORD AND EVELYN WAUGH Nancy Mitford & Evelyn Waugh
LIBRA Don DeLillo
A LIFE IN LETTERS John Steinbeck
LIFE IS A DREAM Gyula Krúdy
LIGHT YEARS James Salter
LITTLE BIRDS Anaïs Nin
A LITTLE LEARNING: THE FIRST VOLUME OF AN AUTOBIOGRAPHY Evelyn Waugh
A LITTLE ORDER Evelyn Waugh
LIVE AND LET DIE Ian Fleming
THE LOG FROM THE SEA OF CORTEZ John Steinbeck
LOLITA Vladimir Nabokov
LONDON BELONGS TO ME Norman Collins
THE LONELY LONDONERS Sam Selvon
LONESOME TRAVELER Jack Kerouac
THE LONG VALLEY John Steinbeck

THE MAN-EATER OF MALGUDI R. K. Narayan
MANHATTAN TRANSFER John Dos Passos
MAN'S FATE André Malraux
MANTICORE Robertson Davies
MAPP AND LUCIA E. F. Benson
MARRY ME John Updike
MARY Vladimir Nabokov
THE MASK OF DIMITRIOS Eric Ambler
MASS PSYCHOLOGY Sigmund Freud
THE MEDIUM IS THE MASSAGE Marshall McLuhan & Quentin Fiore
THE MEMBER OF THE WEDDING Carson McCullers
MEMOIRS Tennessee Williams
MEMOIRS OF A DUTIFUL DAUGHTER Simone de Beauvoir
MEMOIRS OF HADRIAN Marguerite Yourcenar
MEMORIES OF THE FORD ADMINISTRATION John Updike
MEN AT ARMS Evelyn Waugh
MEPHISTO Klaus Mann
THE MERRY-GO-ROUND IN THE SEA Randolph Stow
THE MERSEY SOUND Adrian Henri, Roger McGough & Brian Patten
METAMORPHOSIS AND OTHER STORIES Franz Kafka
THE MIDDLE PARTS OF FORTUNE Frederic Manning
MISTER PARADISE Tennessee Williams

A MIXTURE OF FRAILTIES Robertson Davies
MODERN TIMES Jean-Paul Sartre
MOLESWORTH Geoffrey Willans & Ronald Searle
MOMENTS OF REPRIEVE Primo Levi
MONKEY GRIP Helen Garner
THE MONKEY WRENCH GANG Edward Abbey
A MONTH IN THE COUNTRY J. L. Carr
A MONTH OF SUNDAYS John Updike
THE MOON IS DOWN John Steinbeck
MOON TIGER Penelope Lively
MOONRAKER Ian Fleming
MORE DIE OF HEARTBREAK Saul Bellow
THE MORTGAGED HEART Carson McCullers
MOSES ASCENDING Sam Selvon
THE MOUNTAINS OF MY LIFE Walter Bonatti
MR SAMMLER'S PLANET Saul Bellow
MRS DALLOWAY Virginia Woolf
A MURDER OF QUALITY * John le Carré
MUSIC FOR CHAMELEONS Truman Capote
MY AUTOBIOGRAPHY Charles Chaplin
MY EDUCATION William S. Burroughs
MY HAPPY DAYS IN HELL György Faludy
MY NAME IS ASHER LEV Chaim Potok
MY OEDIPUS COMPLEX Frank O'Connor
THE MYTH OF SISYPHUS Albert Camus

NADJA André Breton
NAUSEA Jean-Paul Sartre
THE NEEDLE'S EYE * Margaret Drabble
NEW AND COLLECTED POEMS 1931–2001 Czesław Miłosz
NIGHT Elie Wiesel
NIKOLAI GOGOL Vladimir Nabokov
NINETEEN EIGHTY-FOUR George Orwell
NO EASY WALK TO FREEDOM Nelson Mandela
NO LONGER AT EASE Chinua Achebe
NOBODY KNOWS MY NAME James Baldwin
NORTH OF SOUTH Shiva Naipul
NOVA EXPRESS William S. Burroughs
NUMBERS IN THE DARK Italo Calvino

OCTOPUSSY *and* THE LIVING DAYLIGHTS Ian Fleming
OF LOVE AND HUNGER Julian Ross-Maclaren
OF MICE AND MEN John Steinbeck
OFFICERS AND GENTLEMEN Evelyn Waugh
OIL! Upton Sinclair
OLD MASTERS Thomas Bernhard
THE OLD PATAGONIAN EXPRESS Paul Theroux
OLEANDER, JACARANDA Penelope Lively
ON BROADWAY Damon Runyon
ON GRIEF AND REASON * Joseph Brodsky
ON HER MAJESTY'S SECRET SERVICE Ian Fleming

ON MURDER, MOURNING AND MELANCHOLIA Sigmund Freud
ON PHOTOGRAPHY Susan Sontag
ON THE ROAD Jack Kerouac
ON THE ROAD: THE ORIGINAL SCROLL Jack Kerouac
ONCE A JAILBIRD * Hans Fallada
ONCE THERE WAS A WAR John Steinbeck
ONE DAY IN THE LIFE OF IVAN DENISOVICH Aleksandr Solzhenitsyn
ONE FAT ENGLISHMAN * Kingsley Amis
ONE FLEW OVER THE CUCKOO'S NEST Ken Kesey
ONE HUNDRED YEARS OF SOLITUDE Gabriel García Márquez
ONE-WAY STREET AND OTHER WRITINGS Walter Benjamin
THE ORDEAL OF GILBERT PINFOLD Evelyn Waugh
ORIENTALISM Edward W. Said
ORLANDO Virginia Woolf
ORWELL AND POLITICS George Orwell
THE ORWELL DIARIES George Orwell
ORWELL IN SPAIN George Orwell
ORWELL'S ENGLAND George Orwell
OTHER VOICES, OTHER ROOMS Truman Capote
OUR TOWN AND OTHER PLAYS Thornton Wilder
OUT OF AFRICA Isak Dinesen (Karen Blixen)
THE OUTSIDER Albert Camus

THE OUTSIDERS S. E. Hinton
OVER TO YOU Roald Dahl

THE PAINTER OF SIGNS R. K. Narayan
PALE FIRE Vladimir Nabokov
PALE HORSE, PALE RIDER * Katherine Anne Porter
PARADE'S END Ford Madox Ford
PARADISE POSTPONED John Mortimer
THE PASTURES OF HEAVEN John Steinbeck
THE PATH TO THE SPIDERS' NESTS Italo Calvino
THE PEARL John Steinbeck
THE PENGUIN FREUD READER Sigmund Freud / Adam Phillips (Editor)
THE PERFECT MURDER * H. R. F. Keating
PERFUME Patrick Süskind
THE PERIODIC TABLE Primo Levi
PETALS OF BLOOD Ngũgĩ wa Thiong'o
THE PHILOSOPHY OF ANDY WARHOL Andy Warhol
PHYSICS AND PHILOSOPHY Werner Heisenberg
THE PLAGUE Albert Camus
PNIN Vladimir Nabokov
POEMS *and* EXILES James Joyce
POET IN NEW YORK Federico García Lorca
POETRY OF THE THIRTIES Robin Skelton (Editor)
THE POORHOUSE FAIR John Updike

POPism Andy Warhol
A Portrait of the Artist as a Young Man James Joyce
The Price Arthur Miller
Pricksongs and Descants * Robert Coover
The Prime of Miss Jean Brodie Muriel Spark
The Prophet Kahlil Gibran
Proud to Be a Mammal Czesław Miłosz
The Psychedelic Experience Timothy Leary, Ralph Metzner & Richard Alpert
The Psychology of Love Sigmund Freud
The Psychopathology of Everyday Life Sigmund Freud
Put Out More Flags Evelyn Waugh

Quantum of Solace Ian Fleming
Quartet Jean Rhys
The Queen's Gambit Walter Tevis
Queer William S. Burroughs

Rabbit at Rest John Updike
Rabbit is Rich John Updike
Rabbit Redux John Updike
Rabbit, Run John Updike
The Radetzky March Joseph Roth

A Rage in Harlem * Chester Himes
The Ragged Trousered Philanthropists Robert Tressell
Ragtime E. L. Doctorow
Ravelstein Saul Bellow
The Real Cool Killers * Chester Himes
The Real Life of Sebastian Knight Vladimir Nabokov
The Rebel Albert Camus
The Red Pony John Steinbeck
Red Strangers Elspeth Huxley
Reflections in a Golden Eye Carson McCullers
Remote People Evelyn Waugh
The Reprieve Jean-Paul Sartre
Rhinoceros, The Chairs, The Lesson Eugene Ionesco
The Road to San Giovanni Italo Calvino
The Road to Wigan Pier George Orwell
Roger's Version John Updike
The Room * Hubert Selby Jr
A Room of One's Own Virginia Woolf
A Room of One's Own / Three Guineas Virginia Woolf
The Rose Tattoo and Other Plays Tennessee Williams
The Royal Hunt of the Sun Peter Shaffer

The Russia House * John le Carré
A Russian Journal John Steinbeck

S. John Updike
Say a Little Mantra for Me Yvonne Burgess
Scent of a Woman * Giovanni Arpino
The Scent of Dried Roses Tim Lott
A Science Fiction Omnibus Brian Aldiss (Editor)
Scoop Evelyn Waugh
The Sea is My Brother Jack Kerouac
Season of Migration to the North Tayeb Salih
The Secret Pilgrim * John le Carré
Seize the Day Saul Bellow
Selected Plays W. B. Yeats
Selected Poems Jorge Luis Borges
Selected Poems Paul Celan
Selected Poems Patrick Kavanagh
Selected Poems Federico García Lorca
Selected Poems Osip Mandelstam
Selected Poems Pablo Neruda
Selected Poems Fernando Pessoa
Selected Poems Rainer Maria Rilke
Selected Poems Stevie Smith
Selected Poems Dylan Thomas
Selected Poems R. S. Thomas
Selected Poems William Carlos Williams

SELECTED POEMS W. B. Yeats
SELECTED POEMS 1947–1995 Allen Ginsberg
SELECTED SHORT STORIES Virginia Woolf
SELF-PORTRAIT * Man Ray
SERGEANT LAMB OF THE NINTH Robert Graves
SEVEN DAYS IN NEW CRETE Robert Graves
SEVEN GOTHIC TALES Isak Dinesen (Karen Blixen)
SEVEN PILLARS OF WISDOM T. E. Lawrence
THE SEVEN SISTERS * Margaret Drabble
SHADOWS ON THE GRASS Isak Dinesen (Karen Blixen)
SHAH OF SHAHS Ryszard Kapuściński
THE SHELTERING SKY Paul Bowles
SHIP OF FOOLS * Katherine Anne Porter
THE SHIRALEE D'Arcy Niland
SHOOTING AN ELEPHANT AND OTHER ESSAYS George Orwell
THE SHOOTING PARTY Isabel Colegate
A SHORT HISTORY OF DECAY E. M. Cioran
THE SHORT REIGN OF PIPPIN IV John Steinbeck
SIDDHARTHA Hermann Hesse
SILENT SPRING Rachel Carson
SIMONE WEIL: AN ANTHOLOGY Simone Weil
SISTER CARRIE Theodore Dreiser
SIX CHARACTERS IN SEARCH OF AN AUTHOR AND OTHER PLAYS Luigi Pirandello

Six Memos for the Next Millennium Italo Calvino
Sixty Stories Donald Barthelme
A Small Circus Hans Fallada
A Small Town in Germany * John le Carré
Snow Country Yasunari Kawabata
The Snows of Yesteryear Gregor von Rezzori
Solo Faces James Salter
Someone Like You Roald Dahl
The Sound of the Mountain Yasunari Kawabata
The Sound of Trumpets John Mortimer
South from Granada Gerald Brenan
Southern Mail / Night Flight Antoine de Saint-Exupéry
Speak, Memory Vladimir Nabokov
The Spider's House Paul Bowles
A Spy in the House of Love Anaïs Nin
The Spy Who Came in from the Cold John le Carré
The Spy Who Loved Me Ian Fleming
St Trinian's Ronald Searle
Steppenwolf Hermann Hesse
The Stones of Florence and Venice Observed Mary McCarthy

STORM OF STEEL Ernst Jünger
STORY OF A SECRET STATE Jan Karski
STORY OF THE EYE Georges Bataille
STRAIT IS THE GATE André Gide
A STREETCAR NAMED DESIRE Tennessee Williams
STRONG OPINIONS Vladimir Nabokov
STUDIES IN HYSTERIA Sigmund Freud
STYLES OF RADICAL WILL Susan Sontag
THE SUBTERRANEANS Jack Kerouac
SUDDENLY LAST SUMMER AND OTHER PLAYS Tennessee Williams
SUMMER CROSSING Truman Capote
SWEET BIRD OF YOUTH AND OTHER PLAYS Tennessee Williams
SWEET THURSDAY John Steinbeck
SWORD OF HONOUR Evelyn Waugh

TARKA THE OTTER Henry Williamson
TARRY FLYNN Patrick Kavanagh
TEMPEST-TOST Robertson Davies
TENDER IS THE NIGHT F. Scott Fitzgerald
TERRA AMATA J. M. G. Le Clézio
THE TERROR OF ST TRINIAN'S AND OTHER DRAWINGS Ronald Searle
THE THEORY OF THE MODERN STAGE Eric Bentley (Editor)

TRAVELS WITH CHARLEY John Steinbeck
THE TRIAL Franz Kafka
THE TUNNEL * Ernesto Sábato

U.S.A. John Dos Passos
ULYSSES James Joyce
THE UNCANNY Sigmund Freud
UNCOMMON DANGER Eric Ambler
UNCONDITIONAL SURRENDER Evelyn Waugh
THE UNCONSCIOUS Sigmund Freud
UNCONVENTIONAL REMINISCENCES William Scully
UNDER A MONSOON CLOUD * H. R. F. Keating
UNDER FIRE Henri Barbusse
UNDER MILK WOOD Dylan Thomas
UNDER THE BANYAN TREE AND OTHER STORIES R. K. Narayan
UNDER THE JAGUAR SUN Italo Calvino
UNDER THE SIGN OF SATURN Susan Sontag
UNDER THE VOLCANO Malcolm Lowry
THE UNDERGROUND MAN * Ross Macdonald
UNDERTONES OF WAR Edmund Blunden
A UNIVERSAL HISTORY OF INIQUITY Jorge Luis Borges
UNTOUCHABLE Mulk Raj Anand
UP ABOVE THE WORLD Paul Bowles
THE USES OF LITERACY Richard Hoggart

WILD ANALYSIS Sigmund Freud
THE WILD BOYS William S. Burroughs
WIND, SAND AND STARS Antoine de Saint-Exupéry
THE WINTER OF OUR DISCONTENT John Steinbeck
WINTER'S TALES Isak Dinesen (Karen Blixen)
THE WITCHES OF EASTWICK John Updike
WOLF SOLENT John Cowper Powys
THE 'WOLFMAN' AND OTHER CASES Sigmund Freud
THE WOMAN IN THE DUNES Kobo Abe
WORDS Jean-Paul Sartre
WORK SUSPENDED AND OTHER STORIES Evelyn Waugh
WORLD OF WONDERS Robertson Davies
WRITINGS ON IRISH FOLKLORE, LEGEND AND MYTH W. B. Yeats

THE YAGE LETTERS Allen Ginsberg & William S. Burroughs
THE YEARS Virginia Woolf
YOU ONLY LIVE TWICE Ian Fleming

ZAZIE IN THE METRO Queneau, Raymond
ZENO'S CONSCIENCE Italo Svevo

Mini Modern Classics

Ryūnosuke Akutagawa *Hell Screen*
Kingsley Amis *Dear Illusion*
Donald Barthelme *Some of Us Had Been Threatening Our Friend Colby*
Samuel Beckett *The Expelled*
Saul Bellow *Him With His Foot in His Mouth*
Jorge Luis Borges *The Widow Ching – Pirate*
Paul Bowles *The Delicate Prey*
Italo Calvino *The Queen's Necklace*
Albert Camus *The Adulterous Woman*
Truman Capote *Children on Their Birthdays*
Angela Carter *Bluebeard*
Raymond Chandler *Killer in the Rain*
Eileen Chang *Red Rose, White Rose*
G. K. Chesterton *The Strange Crime of John Boulnois*
Joseph Conrad *Youth*
Robert Coover *Romance of the Thin Man and the Fat Lady*
Isak Dinesen [Karen Blixen] *Babette's Feast*
Margaret Drabble *The Gifts of War*
Hans Fallada *Short Treatise on the Joys of Morphinism*
F. Scott Fitzgerald *Babylon Revisited*
Ian Fleming *The Living Daylights*
E. M. Forster *The Machine Stops*
Shirley Jackson *The Tooth*
Henry James *The Beast in the Jungle*

M. R. James *Canon Alberic's Scrap-Book*
James Joyce *Two Gallants*
Franz Kafka *In the Penal Colony*
Rudyard Kipling *'They'*
D. H. Lawrence *Odour of Chrysanthemums*
Primo Levi *The Magic Paint*
H. P. Lovecraft *The Colour Out of Space*
Malcolm Lowry *Lunar Caustic*
Katherine Mansfield *Bliss*
Carson McCullers *Wunderkind*
Robert Musil *Flypaper*
Vladimir Nabokov *Terra Incognita*
R. K. Narayan *A Breath of Lucifer*
Frank O'Connor *The Cornet-Player Who Betrayed Ireland*
Dorothy Parker *The Sexes*
Ludmilla Petrushevskaya *Through the Wall*
Jean Rhys *La Grosse Fifi*
Saki *Filboid Studge, the Story of a Mouse That Helped*
Isaac Bashevis Singer *The Last Demon*
William Trevor *The Mark-2 Wife*
John Updike *Rich in Russia*
H. G. Wells *The Door in the Wall*
Eudora Welty *Moon Lake*
P. G. Wodehouse *The Crime Wave at Blandings*
Virginia Woolf *The Lady in the Looking-Glass*
Stefan Zweig *Chess*

Reader's Notes